First published in Great Britain in 2006 by HarperCollins Children's Books.
HarperCollins Children's Books is a division of HarperCollins Publishers Ltd.

1 3 5 7 9 10 8 6 4 2

ISBN-13: 978-0-00-724018-0
ISBN: 0-00-724018-X

WALT DISNEY PICTURES AND WALDEN MEDIA PRESENT "THE CHRONICLES OF NARNIA: THE LION, THE WITCH AND THE WARDROBE" BASED ON THE BOOK BY C.S. LEWIS

A MARK JOHNSON PRODUCTION AN ANDREW ADAMSON FILM MUSIC COMPOSED BY HARRY GREGSON-WILLIAMS COSTUME DESIGNER ISIS MUSSENDEN EDITED BY SIM EVAN-JONES PRODUCTION DESIGNER ROGER FORD

DIRECTOR OF PHOTOGRAPHY DONALD M. McALPINE, ASC, ACS CO-PRODUCER DOUGLAS GRESHAM EXECUTIVE PRODUCERS ANDREW ADAMSON PERRY MOORE

WALDEN MEDIA SCREENPLAY BY ANN PEACOCK AND ANDREW ADAMSON AND CHRISTOPHER MARKUS & STEPHEN McFEELY PRODUCED BY MARK JOHNSON PHILIP STEUER DIRECTED BY ANDREW ADAMSON Walt Disney Pictures

Distributed by BUENA VISTA PICTURES DISTRIBUTION THE CHRONICLES OF NARNIA, NARNIA, and all book titles, characters and locales original thereto are trademarks of C.S. Lewis Pte Ltd. and are used with permission. ©Disney Enterprises, Inc. and Walden Media, LLC. All rights reserved.

Narnia.com

A CIP catalogue for this title is available from the British Library.

The HarperCollins website address is: www.harpercollinschildrensbooks.co.uk

Printed and bound in Spain

-The Chronicles of- NARNIA

ACTIVITY BOOK

HarperCollins *Children's Books*

Welcome to the enchanted world of Narnia. A magical place, home to fauns, dryads, talking beasts, evil witches and magnificent heroes, as well as several ordinary boys and girls.

From Narnia's very beginning, witnessed by Polly and Digory, to the epic battle between the Pevensies and the White Witch, King Caspian's seafaring adventure aboard the Dawn Treader to Eustace and Jill's efforts to save Narnia from the wicked Tash, Sons of Adam and Daughters of Eve have always come to Narnia in times of great trouble.

This very special activity book also includes a section about The Chronicles of Narnia; The Lion, the Witch and the Wardrobe movie from Disney and Walden Media. Learn more about the special effects in the movie, why the Pevensie children were evacuated from London and the author of The Chronicles of Narnia, C.S. Lewis.

Discover the magical history behind the prophecies, learn how the White Witch came to threaten the peaceful land and follow the adventures of Aslan, the true king. The Chronicles of Narnia Annual is full of puzzles, posters, games and activities to help you learn a little more about the Deep Magic of Narnia…

Contents

The Magician's Nephew

When Digory and Polly find Uncle Andrew's private study, they not only stumble on a family secret but also discover a magical way to travel to other worlds.

First, the pair find themselves in the desolate land of Charn and awaken an evil witch, Jadis, who tricks the children into returning to England with her in tow. Realising they need to get the wicked queen out of their world, Polly and Digory use Uncle Andrew's magic rings to transport themselves, Jadis, Uncle Andrew, Frank, the coachman, and his horse, Strawberry, to the Wood Between Worlds and then into a new world.

This newborn world is in fact Narnia, and is being sung into life by Aslan the lion. Having brought the evil Jadis into Narnia, Aslan tasks Sons of Adam and Daughters of Eve with the job of protecting Narnia from her future threats. Join Polly and Digory on this enchanting adventure at the very birth of Narnia…

The Birth of Narnia

Narnia was an empty and desolate land until Aslan made it come alive. Draw in all the trees, rivers and talking beasts as Aslan sings Narnia into life.

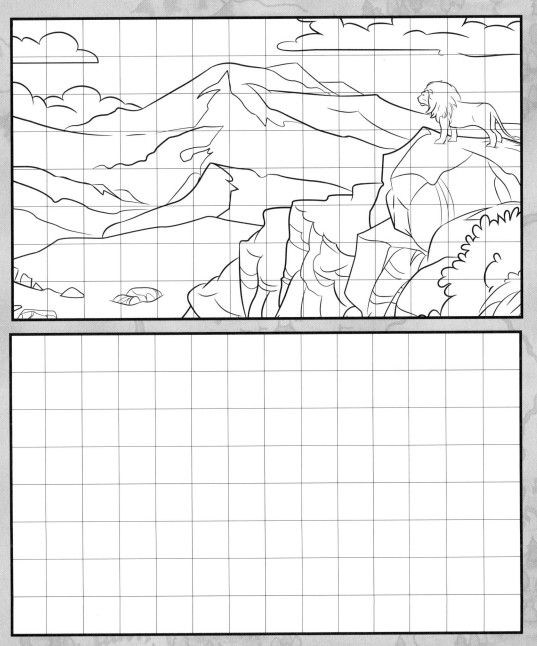

Narnia Riddles

Answer these riddles to reveal some of the deep secrets from the beginning of time.

Once back in London, Jadis used this horse to attack the policemen

Y S T R R R A B E W

_ _ _ _ _ _ _ _ _

④

Uncle Andrew used these to send Polly and Digory into different worlds

G N I S R

_ _ _ _ _

①

Uncle Andrew, Polly, Digory and Frank saw this lion singing the land to life

L N A S A

_ _ _ _ _

⑤

In the wood between the worlds, the children travelled through these

O L O S P

_ _ _ _ _

②

This grew in the ground after Jadis threw it at the lion

A M L P O T S P

_ _ _ _ _ _ _

⑥

Polly and Digory released this evil Queen from an enchanted sleep

S J A D I

_ _ _ _ _

③

The land Jadis thought to be empty was in fact just being born and was called

A N R A I N

_ _ _ _ _ _ ⑦

The first flying horse of Narnia

D L E F G E

_ _ _ _ _ _ ⑧

The first Son of Adam and Daughter of Eve, King and Queen of Narnia

K N A F R and L L E N H

⑪ _ _ _ _ _ and

_ _ _ _ _

The lion sent Digory on a mission to find this to protect Narnia

P L P A E

_ _ _ _ _ ⑨

Once back home, Digory gave his mother an enchanted apple then buried the core in his garden. When he grew up and moved, he used the wood of the magical tree to build this

D R W B O R E A

⑫ _ _ _ _ _ _ _

Jadis hid here and tried to tempt Digory after eating forbidden apples

A R R C H D O

_ _ _ _ _ _ ⑩

The Magician's Nephew Wordsearch

Can you find all these words in the grid below?

C	Z	J	G	Y	G	F	Y	R	S	A	I	D	I	P
G	P	N	Q	R	I	L	H	T	C	S	N	E	Q	H
U	I	Y	E	V	L	M	R	Y	O	L	E	P	L	M
R	N	E	C	O	J	A	D	I	S	A	L	L	N	H
Z	N	C	P	H	W	X	H	F	U	N	E	O	D	C
P	P	C	L	B	A	F	J	E	X	L	H	R	Y	E
X	R	L	E	E	W	R	D	U	T	I	P	A	Q	G
A	J	R	C	M	A	O	N	Q	G	M	J	B	W	D
G	R	S	F	E	Z	N	L	W	C	T	Z	L	Y	E
Y	P	Z	K	B	O	R	D	L	N	K	T	E	K	L
I	I	Q	K	N	Y	X	N	R	E	B	L	H	X	F
K	A	W	M	I	A	W	I	F	E	Y	Q	F	M	N
Y	R	O	G	I	D	R	V	P	I	W	Z	W	F	X
P	K	Q	N	A	F	W	F	B	E	W	A	N	E	U
E	L	P	P	A	O	D	U	Y	N	L	P	O	Y	W

- ❑ APPLE
- ❑ ASLAN
- ❑ CHARN
- ❑ DEPLORABLE
- ❑ DIGORY
- ❑ FLEDGE
- ❑ FRANK
- ❑ GREEN
- ❑ HELEN
- ❑ JADIS
- ❑ POLLY
- ❑ RING
- ❑ STRAWBERRY
- ❑ UNCLEANDREW
- ❑ YELLOW

The Lion, the Witch and the Wardrobe

When Lucy Pevensie ducks into a wardrobe during a game of hide-and-seek, she never expects to be transported to another world. A world of magic, enchantment and fear.

Narnia is under the rule of the Jadis, White Witch, and has been in eternal winter for a hundred years but there is a prophecy. It is foretold that two Sons of Adam and two Daughters of Eve will end the White Witch's tyrannical reign and bring Aslan, the true lion king of Narnia, back to the land. While all of Narnia know the Witch to be evil, Lucy's brother, Edmund, falls for her cunning lies and soon betrays his family.

With the help of a faun, some friendly beavers and Aslan, Lucy and her brothers and sister challenge Jadis and her wicked army, But can four children really defeat this powerful Witch and return peace to Narnia?

Friend or Foe?

Edmund thinks he has made a friend in Narnia.

Join the dots to discover who it is.

The Lion, the Witch and the Wardrobe Crossword

CLUES

Across

1. This was always lit, where the children entered Narnia
7. The children were sent away to stay with this man
8. Lucy first travelled through this into Narnia
9. The captain of the Secret Police

Down

2. Lucy's first friend in Narnia
3. These creatures helped the Pevensies when they all came to Narnia
4. He gave the children special gifts
5. Where Aslan was killed
6. Edmund loved to eat this
7. The eldest Pevensie

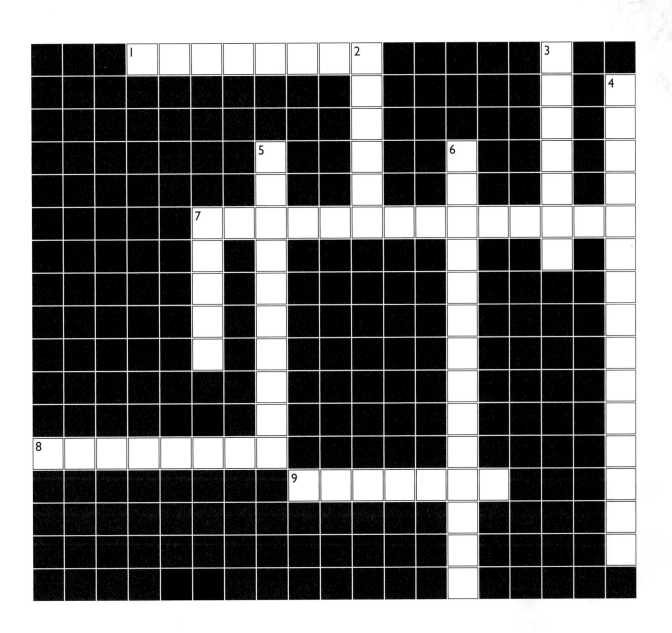

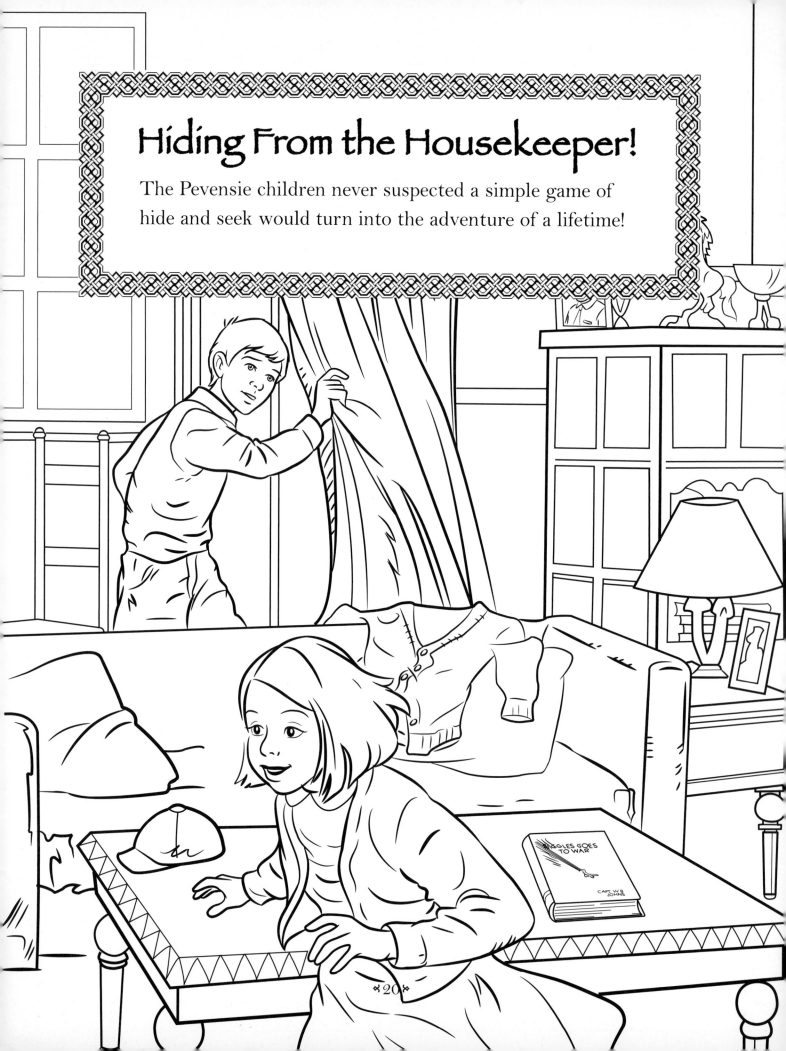

Hiding From the Housekeeper!

The Pevensie children never suspected a simple game of hide and seek would turn into the adventure of a lifetime!

Spot the Difference

The White Witch is slain but Edmund is in danger.
Can Lucy save him with her magical cordial?

There are five differences between these two pictures
– can you spot them all?

Friend or Foe?

Peter, Susan and Lucy meet a creature in the woods who claims to be a friend. Can they trust him? Join the dots to find out who the stranger really is.

The Metal Tree

The Kings and Queens of Narnia are hunting the White Stag when they come across something very familiar. Can you find your way through the maze to the lamppost?

The Horse and His Boy

In the Golden Age of Narnia, with High King Peter and his royal family on the throne at Cair Paravel, a young boy named Shasta lives in Calormen with his fisherman father.

Life is hard but uneventful for Shasta until, one night, when a visitor comes looking for shelter and asks his father to sell Shasta as a slave. Shasta overhears that his father is indeed not his father but found him as a small infant and that he is more than prepared to sell him. On hearing this, Shasta makes plans to run away and is assisted by the visitor's horse, Bree, a talking horse that had been captured in Narnia and made to work.

As the pair flee through the capital city of Calormen, Shasta learns that not only is he the double of Prince Corin, but that there is a Calormene plot to invade Narnia. Bree and Shasta must summon all their courage to alert the royal family of Narnia and save the free land to the north. It is only once he has reached the royal family that Shasta learns the true secret of his identity. But can he and Bree save Narnia alone or will they have magical help from Aslan?

The Horse and His Boy
Wordsearch

All the words below are hidden in this grid. Can you find them?

Z	X	S	I	M	A	H	C	T	H	J	G	T	E	E
P	K	L	F	N	O	A	S	F	N	H	A	I	E	N
O	K	H	V	M	L	S	G	A	V	S	T	S	R	U
H	V	A	Y	O	Z	Y	A	A	D	D	R	R	B	L
O	R	O	R	A	D	K	G	R	T	A	K	O	Q	G
D	C	M	X	A	R	B	H	S	J	I	B	C	S	N
Y	E	Z	K	A	L	C	L	H	R	C	M	A	H	I
N	J	P	T	H	B	L	H	E	S	N	G	R	R	K
N	A	A	B	H	S	A	T	E	D	H	N	T	E	T
A	I	N	R	A	N	R	D	S	N	H	A	B	A	H
M	O	Q	F	H	B	Q	C	H	I	L	H	S	Z	E
P	R	I	N	C	E	C	O	R	I	N	A	Y	T	E
N	H	T	A	R	A	V	I	S	M	L	B	N	Y	A
R	C	X	J	T	U	B	J	T	E	B	J	C	D	M
I	B	K	K	E	V	N	B	S	E	T	Y	N	O	L

❏ ANVARD   ❏ CALORMEN   ❏ RABADASH

❏ ARAVIS   ❏ HERMIT   ❏ SHASTA

❏ ARCHENLAND   ❏ KINGLUNE   ❏ TARKAAN

❏ ARSHEESH   ❏ NARNIA   ❏ TASHBAAN

❏ BREE   ❏ PRINCECORIN   ❏ TISROC

Prince Caspian

Peter, Susan, Edmund and Lucy Pevensie are not looking forward to returning to school but when they least expect it, they are pulled from the train platform and transported back to the magical land of Narnia.

But this is not the rich and pleasant land they ruled over for decades, this Narnia is free of talking beasts, the wood nymphs and dryads are all asleep and Cair Paravel is in ruins. A false Telmarine king sits on the throne and his nephew and the true heir to the Narnian throne, Prince Caspian is in hiding.

Can the royal children find Caspian and reunite all the talking beasts of Narnia in the name of Aslan before Caspian's meagre army are defeated by King Miraz's evil and treacherous hoards? With the help of Aslan and some new friends, Trumpkin the dwarf, Trufflehunter the badger and Reepicheep the mouse, they will do all that they can to save Narnia once more.

Prince Caspian Crossword

CLUES

Across

3. The children's nickname for Trumpkin
4. The false king of Narnia comes from this place

Down

1. Truffelhunter is one of these
2. A mouse and a true hero!
5. The false king and uncle of Caspian

Where Are We?

Peter, Susan, Edmund and Lucy have been magically pulled out of their train carriage but where are they?
Look at the clues then use the code to work out exactly where the children have arrived!

Clues:

• Ruins of a castle
• By the sea
• Ruby studded chessmen
• Treasure room

7 19 4   18 19 12 17 20 16 4 24   5 16 4
12 24   24 5 16 24 12 5!

7 19 4   16 25 12 24 22   5 16 4
18 5 12 16   13 5 16 5 1 4 17.

_ _ _   _ _ _ _ _ _ _   _ _ _

_ _   _ _ _ _ _

_ _ _   _ _ _ _ _   _ _ _

_ _ _ _   _ _ _ _ _ _

Code:

A	B	C	D	E	F	G	H	I	J
5	11	18	20	4	26	10	19	12	21

K	L	M	N	O	P	Q	R	S	T
6	17	9	24	3	13	23	16	22	7

U	V	W	X	Y	Z
25	1	15	14	8	2

In Search of the Gifts

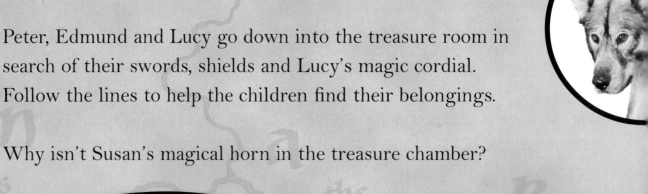

Peter, Edmund and Lucy go down into the treasure room in search of their swords, shields and Lucy's magic cordial. Follow the lines to help the children find their belongings.

Why isn't Susan's magical horn in the treasure chamber?

Friends of Narnia

Narnia has found many friends in the Sons of Adam and Daughters of Eve. Can you find them all in this wordsearch below?

R	Z	O	K	N	R	E	J	H	T
Y	U	K	A	P	E	D	P	U	X
L	L	S	O	U	T	M	R	H	T
V	U	L	D	Z	E	U	F	O	U
S	L	J	O	I	P	N	E	U	S
Y	A	O	I	M	G	D	H	I	X
L	U	C	Y	L	X	O	W	D	G
Z	K	L	R	Q	L	R	R	C	S
E	U	S	T	A	C	E	Z	Y	R
A	F	V	K	K	N	A	R	F	M

❑ DIGORY ❑ JILL ❑ PETER

❑ EDMUND ❑ LUCY ❑ POLLY

❑ EUSTACE ❑ MOLLY ❑ SUSAN

❑ FRANK

Who Can Lucy See?

While the others are all asleep, Lucy sees something in the woods. Join the dots to see who has a message for Lucy.

Enemies of Aslan

There are some evil things in Narnia, witches, beasts, creatures and even some men. Can you find all these enemies of Aslan in this wordsearch?

H	X	U	Z	S	K	N	J	I	G	E	W	V	T	V
J	U	E	H	A	G	L	U	Z	T	U	M	E	I	H
K	A	I	Z	O	R	O	A	I	Y	A	O	R	S	S
X	F	D	T	C	Q	I	R	P	U	C	H	G	L	I
T	S	I	I	C	K	P	M	G	E	S	C	O	M	M
Y	J	U	C	S	S	U	R	A	A	O	O	G	B	H
B	D	Q	B	A	U	I	F	T	W	I	A	H	N	B
Z	H	A	A	U	M	B	O	W	S	M	T	D	H	O
W	K	D	B	M	C	J	A	M	J	N	I	Q	R	U
L	O	D	E	N	Z	N	F	H	Z	V	R	X	A	C
A	D	I	H	S	I	R	I	T	D	R	A	G	O	N
K	P	U	F	R	D	L	S	I	C	J	Z	O	P	G
X	B	T	X	U	D	O	O	A	X	F	P	A	W	G
R	O	K	M	Z	Z	K	B	R	U	B	U	G	E	G
K	T	W	V	A	F	S	T	W	T	N	A	I	G	W

- ❏ APE
- ❏ DRAGON
- ❏ GIANT
- ❏ HAG
- ❏ INCUBUS
- ❏ JADIS
- ❏ MAUGRIM
- ❏ MIRAZ
- ❏ OGRE
- ❏ RISHIDA
- ❏ SHIFT
- ❏ SPRITE
- ❏ TASH
- ❏ TIRAZ
- ❏ WRAITH

Through the Woods

The children and Trumpkin the dwarf must set out to Prince Caspian's camp with Aslan's guidance but only Lucy can see him! Help them all safely through the maze.

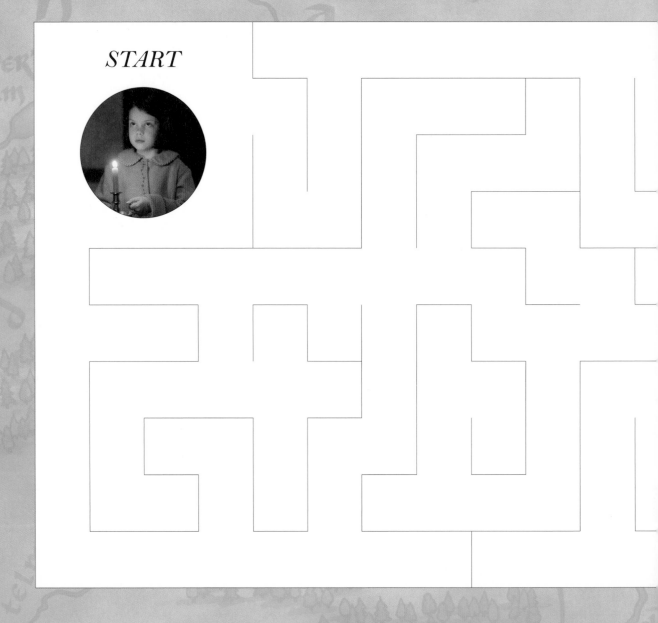

START

FINISH

Voyage of the Dawn Treader

The idea of spending summer with their know-it-all cousin Eustace Scrubb is not at all appealing to Lucy and Edmund but little do they realise this is not the summer Aslan has in store of them. Soon the three cousins are pulled through a magical painting and aboard the Dawn Treader, ship of King Caspian the tenth.

Ten years have passed since their last visit to Narnia and the land is at peace under Caspian, but affairs in the islands belonging to Narnia are not all so well. Caspian is on a mission to find the seven good lords of Narnia who were sent away by his evil uncle, Miraz, before he killed Caspian's father.

The companions must face slave traders, magicians, invisible Dufflepuds and evil enchanted islands before they can account for all seven Lords and return to Narnia. While Lucy and Edmund are excited to be back, Edmund has some tough lessons to learn and must accept Narnia and Aslan into his heart before he can change. There are hard lessons for everyone on the voyage across Narnia's high seas as the magic of the chronicles continues.

Voyage of the Dawn Treader Crossword

CLUES

Across

4. Lucy and Edmund's cousin

5. The children enter Narnia through this

Down

1. Eustace turns into one

2. The lord that bought King Caspian

3. The name of the star who oversees the three sleeping lords

True or False?

1. Eustace is spending the summer with Peter and Susan

2. King Caspian is looking for the seven Lords of Narnia

3. Reepicheep is hoping to find the White Witch

4. Caspian and the children are captured as salves in the Lone Islands

5. Caspian is bought and released by Lord Bern of Narnia

6. After the Dawn Treader is caught in a storm, they arrive at an island inhabited by giants

7. Eustace turns into a dragon and is saved by Aslan

8. Edmund claims an island that turns everything into solid silver

9. Lucy casts a spell that makes her beautiful

10. Lucy casts a spell to make the Dufflepuds visible

11. Caspian finds the last three Lords in an enchanted sleep

12. The island is home to Ramandu, a former star

13. Reepicheep offers to sail to the end of the world and never return

14. When the children and Reepicheep leave the Dawn Treader, the water is full of seaweed

15. On land, the children meet a lamb who is in fact, Aslan

The Silver Chair

Eustace Scrubb is a changed man but together with his friend Jill Pole, he attends a public school where is a target of the class bullies. Without warning, the pair are pulled out of the path of Edith Jackle the bully and cast back into Narnia.

Here he finds King Caspian an old man, broken by the death of his wife and the kidnap of his son. Eustace and Jill are tasked by Aslan to recover Prince Rilian and restore him to the throne of Narnia.

The Parliament of Owls set the pair off on their quest with the help of Puddleglum the Marsh-Wiggle, and the group set off for the dangerous Underland to recover Rilian. The quest takes them into the path of human eating giants, gnomes, knights and finally, the wicked Witch-Queen who holds Caspian hostage. Will they be able to defeat her hypnotic magic and stay true to Aslan and Narnia?

The Silver Chair Wordsearch

Can you find all these words in the grid below?

R	D	A	S	L	A	N	M	S	I	E	X	S	F	E
E	M	E	N	E	U	Z	T	X	L	I	N	O	X	C
H	G	R	E	B	L	N	E	T	G	O	E	P	G	O
T	N	D	B	P	A	G	R	C	W	Y	E	T	O	A
A	A	G	F	I	R	I	G	F	A	R	Q	Y	G	L
E	F	T	G	P	K	E	L	I	I	T	T	D	M	B
F	R	O	Q	N	E	A	A	M	W	Q	S	P	G	L
M	A	R	E	F	K	P	E	L	E	H	J	U	J	A
I	H	E	J	E	Y	N	A	L	M	J	S	R	E	C
L	R	C	M	I	T	N	N	Y	G	S	S	R	G	K
G	U	V	K	H	L	G	N	E	M	H	T	R	A	E
V	Q	B	O	A	O	L	X	J	E	G	P	B	X	M
S	P	U	K	E	J	M	M	C	E	N	F	S	I	E
B	S	N	A	I	L	L	I	R	E	C	N	I	R	P
E	P	U	D	D	L	E	G	L	U	M	X	N	M	R

❑ APE

❑ COALBLACK

❑ DEEPREALM

❑ EARTHMEN

❑ EUSTACE

❑ EXPERIMENT

❑ HOUSE

❑ GIANTS

❑ GLIMFEATHER

❑ GREENKIRTLE

❑ HARFANG

❑ JILL

❑ MARSHWIGGLES

❑ PRINCERILLIAN

❑ PUDDLEGLUM

❑ SNOWFLAKE

Narnia Riddles

Eustace and Jill met many creatures on their adventure in The Silver Chair. Cross out the word Narnia wherever it appears to reveal what they are looking for.

```
JINARNIALLNARNIAAN
NARNIADEUNARNIANAR
NIASTNARNIAACNARN
IAEANARNIARENAR
NIALONARNIAOKNARNI
AINNARNIAGFORPRNARNI
AINCNARNIAERILINARNI
AANNARNIATHETRNARN
IAUEHNARNIAEIRTNARN
IANARNIAOTHNARNIAETH
NARNIARONARNIANE
```

```
PUASLADASLANDLEA
SLANGLUMTASLAHE
MARASLANSWIGASL
ANGASLALEASLANAS
LANHEASLANLTHAS
LANECHIASLANLD
RENLASLANOOKFOR
PRIASLANNCERIAS
LANLIAN
```

The children are not alone in their quest! Cross out the word Aslan wherever it appears to reveal the name of their friend.

The Witch Queen of the Underworld is keeping the Prince captive. Cross out the word Eustace every time it appears to find out how they escaped.

```
P E U S T A C E U E U S T A C E D
D L E G E U S T A C E E U S T A C E L
U M R E U S T A C E E F U S E D T O
E U S T A C E G I V E E U S T A C E
U P B E L I E U S T A C E E F I E U S T
A C N A S L E U S T A C E A N A E U S
T A C E N D T E U S T A C E H E E
U S T A C E O V E U S T A C E E R
W O E U S T A C E R L D W H I E
U S T A C E C H T U R N E E U S T
A C E D T H E Q U E E U S T A C E
E N I N T O A E U S T A C E S E R
P E U S T A C E E N T T E U S T A C E
H A T T H E E U S T A C E Y K I L E
U S T A C E L E D
```

The Last Battle

In the last days of Narnia, a selfish ape named Shift and a simple donkey called Puzzle found a lion skin in the Lantern Wastes, near Lucy's lamppost. In a terrible lie, Shift dressed Puzzle up in the lion skin and tells the talking beasts of Narnia that Aslan has sold them all as slaves to the Calormenes.

Tirian, the last king of Narnia and his best friend, Jewel the unicorn, realised something was horribly wrong and called for help, which arrives in the shape of Eustace and Jill. But it may already be too late – Shift has invoked the name of Tash, evil vulture god of the Calormenes – and he is on his way, bringing death and destruction to Narnia.

Even with Sons of Adam and Daughters of Eve on their side, the Narnians, led by King Tirian, may not be able to save their beloved land. Can the appearance of the friends of Narnia, Lucy, Edmund, Peter, Polly and Digory do anything to change its fate? Or will all be left to Aslan in this final, great last battle…

The Last Battle Wordsearch

Find all the words below in this grid.

F	H	S	A	T	E	M	R	J	L	V	J	E	J	L
T	A	H	O	M	U	O	G	M	O	N	Z	L	E	R
J	K	R	E	Q	O	A	B	T	O	T	S	G	W	H
J	S	T	S	Ñ	N	O	D	P	P	D	J	G	E	Q
G	H	S	W	I	A	T	V	J	N	G	Y	O	L	Z
Z	D	I	F	Q	G	W	M	A	O	K	K	P	S	R
Y	T	D	W	I	X	H	L	L	R	A	J	V	R	L
E	L	Z	Z	U	P	W	T	P	D	I	G	G	L	E
P	I	Z	A	U	O	Q	S	H	L	S	E	G	I	D
Z	R	Z	B	D	S	Ñ	S	G	A	E	H	R	X	J
J	A	E	A	E	M	I	K	X	C	U	E	I	I	L
F	V	H	G	Q	R	Y	Y	G	W	B	F	F	F	S
X	S	K	I	Ñ	G	T	I	R	I	A	N	F	W	T
F	S	C	Y	L	I	U	S	X	L	M	V	L	B	O
U	J	K	C	S	E	G	T	X	Y	T	I	E	S	G

- ☐ CALDRONPOOL
- ☐ GRIFFLE
- ☐ RISHDA
- ☐ DIGGLE
- ☐ JEWEL
- ☐ ROONWIT
- ☐ EMETH
- ☐ KINGTIRIAN
- ☐ SHADOWLANDS
- ☐ FARSIGHT
- ☐ POGGLE
- ☐ SHIFT
- ☐ GINGER
- ☐ PUZZLE
- ☐ TASH

WALT DISNEY PICTURES AND WALDEN MEDIA
PRESENT
·THE CHRONICLES OF·

NARNIA

THE LION, THE WITCH AND THE WARDROBE

The Chronicles of Narnia: The Lion, the Witch and the Wardrobe is a grand scale, epic adventure set in a breath-taking world at the limits of imagination. Faithfully adapted from C. S. Lewis' timeless novel, it tells the story of four siblings – Lucy, Edmund, Susan, and Peter – sent to live on the estate of a mysterious professor to escape the horrors of the WWII bombing of London. The youngest child, Lucy, accidentally discovers the world of Narnia while playing a game of hide-and-seek. She soon encourages her brothers and sister to journey through the open back of a magical wardrobe to travel to Narnia with her. Narnia is a charming, once-peaceful land inhabited by talking beasts, dwarfs, fauns, centaurs and giants. It has become a world cursed with eternal winter by the evil, but beautiful White Witch Jadis. Under the guidance of a noble and mystical ruler, the magnificent lion Aslan, the children fight to overcome Jadis' powerful hold over Narnia in a spectacular, climactic battle de tined to free Narnia from the icy spell forever.

The Movie

SPECIAL EFFECTS AND CREATURE BUILDERS

Weta Studios of New Zealand, the multi-award-winning team behind the special effects and creatures in the *Lord of the Rings* series, invented over forty different species of creatures for this production.

Yours Ever, C.S. Lewis

Clive Staples Lewis, author of The Chronicles of Narnia, a series of seven books including The Lion, the Witch and the Wardrobe, was born on November 29, 1898 in Belfast, Northern Ireland. He had one brother named Warren. When they were young, the two boys played games and wrote stories about make-believe worlds. They played in a large, carved wardrobe that their grandfather had built out of oak. C. S. Lewis went to college at Oxford University outside of London, England and became a professor there, and then at England's Cambridge University. The first book that C. S. Lewis wrote for children was titled The Lion, the Witch and the Wardrobe. Six other books about Narnia followed, and children around the world began writing C. S. Lewis letters, asking him questions and sending their drawings of Narnia characters. Lewis always replied to his young letter writers. Here are two examples of his letters.

C.S. Lewis

The wardrobe featured in the movie.

Dear Joan . . .
I am so glad you like the Narnian books, and it was nice of you to tell me. There are to be seven stories altogether. The ones which have already come out are:
1. *The Lion, the Witch, and the Wardrobe*
2. *Prince Caspian*
3. *The Voyage of the Dawn Treader*
4. *The Silver Chair*

Some time this year, [letter is dated 1954] Number 5, The Horse and His Boy, will be out; and the 6th, *The Magician's Nephew* has already gone to the printer. (You have no idea how long it takes getting a book printed.) The 7th is already written, but still only in pen-and-ink, and I have not quite decided yet what to call it. Sometimes I think of calling it *The King of Narnia*, and some times, *Night Falls on Narnia*. Which do you think sounds best?

I was at a Zoo last week and saw the real lions.

Yours ever,
C.S. Lewis

Dear Denise,
I am delighted to hear that you liked the Narnian books. There is a map at the end of some of them in some editions. But why not do one yourself! And why not write stories for yourself to fill up the gaps in Narnian history? I've left you plenty of hints – especially where Lucy and the Unicorn are talking...I feel *I* have done all I can!

All good wishes,

Yours,
C.S. Lewis

The World of Narnia

Use this map to find your way through the world of Narnia. Find the locations of the places and events you read about. See if you can find:

- **Cair Paravel**
- **The Western Woods**
- **The Great River**
- **The Stone Table**
- **The Lantern Waste**
- **The Fords of Beruna**

You can also draw your own map of Narnia, showing places and characters you think are important. Keep on the lookout for the White Stag!

Sent Away

The novel *The Lion, the Witch and the Wardrobe* opens with these three sentences:

Once there were four children whose names were Peter, Susan, Edmund, and Lucy. This story is about something that happened to them when they were sent away from London during the war because of the air-raids. They were sent to the house of an old Professor who lived in the heart of the country...

IMAGINE... living in a big city and being told one day that you are being sent away. You don't know to where, or for how long, and neither do your parents. You're being sent away because your city is going to be bombed.

You'll be heading to a place in the country where you've never been before, staying with people you've never met. You don't even know whether they like children! You have a small lunch sack, a gas mask, and a postcard ready to send home to tell your parents where you are. If you're lucky, you'll get to stay with your brothers and sisters.

To all your worried feelings, add the threat of war and the fear of attack, and you might be a bit closer to feeling what Peter, Susan, Edmund, and Lucy probably felt standing on a train platform in London, England, waiting, with thousands of other British children, to travel into the unknown.

Movie artist's concept of the bombing of London.

In 1939, with war about to break out between England and Germany, the British expected major attacks by air on all of Britain's cities. children were evacuated from the city to the safety of the countryside, where bombing would probably not occur. (Evacuation means "moving people away from danger.") Evacuations began September 3rd, 1939 – the day England declared war on Germany. A total of 827,000 school children were evacuated, along with 103,000 teachers and helpers. 524,000 more children under school age went with their mothers.

In the countryside, children were usually met by *billeting officers* (*billet* means "to provide housing for") who took them to foster homes, as did volunteers from the Red Cross and other organizations. These adults assisted children with the care and attention they needed. Children went to foster homes on farms, in cottages, and in mansions (where their care might be left to the servants).

C. S. Lewis himself must have been very moved by the evacuations of children, because he and his brother also took several London children seeking safety from the bombing into their country home.

The fantastic experiences that Peter, Susan, Edmund, and Lucy have once they arrive at the old Professor's house in the country, and the powerful lessons they learn about themselves, are the two most important ingredients of *The Lion, the Witch and the Wardrobe*'s magic –

These government posters urged citizens to take action to protect children.

...MAGIC BASED ON REAL LIFE.

Being Brave

In *The Lion, the Witch and the Wardrobe*, Peter is given a special gift—a shield. This is what Peter's shield looks like:

Shields are an important part of the history of England and Ireland. Images on shields hold special meaning. Some symbols are on this page. What do the symbols on Peter's shield stand for?

SHIELD DESIGNS

St. Andrew's Cross
Resolution
Resolve

Roof of a House
Protection
Faithful Service

Military Belt
Honor

SHIELD ELEMENTS

Holly: *Truth*

Fruit: *Freedom, Peace*

Cinquefoil: *Hope, Joy*

Lion: *Peace, Courage,*
(also, Great Warrior, Chief)

Leopard: *Valiant and Enduring Warrior*

Horse: *Readiness for Duty*

Dog: *Courage, Fidelity, Loyalty*

BACKGROUND COLORS

 Gold: *Generosity*

 Red: *Warrior*

 Green: *Hope*

 Orange: *Worthwhile Ambition*

 Silver or White: *Sincerity, Peace*

 Blue: *Strength, Loyalty*

Turning Words Into Pictures
Make your own storyboard

***The Lion, the Witch and the Wardrobe* will soon be a movie! As a movie is planned, but before it is filmed, scenes are imagined with drawing on a series of panels called a *__storyboard__*.**

Storyboards help filmmakers think about how their movies will look, scene by scene. Each panel of a storyboard can be thought of as a filmed moment or shot.

Storyboards are usually drawn in pen or pencil. But if you don't draw or don't like to, you can use cut-out photos from magazines. Your drawings don't have to be fancy. You can use basic shapes, stick figures and simple backgrounds. You may want to draw out your scenes on index cards before drawing them onto your storyboards, so you can play around with the order of the scenes if you need to.

When you make your storyboards, you are also showing how a scene might be filmed.

Here is some language used with storyboards:

• **CLOSE-UP SHOT:** A shot in which there is very little room between the person and the camera. The person's face will usually look very big in a close-up shot.

• **LONG SHOT:** A shot in which there is much distance between a person and the camera, so that the person in a long shot will look very small.

• **LOW CAMERA SHOT:** A camera angle that looks up at the person, making them look important and powerful.

• **POV SHOT:** A shot seen from the point of view of a character in a scene.

• **PAN:** A steady sweeping movement from one point in a scene to another. Good for showing where a scene is taking place and often used at the beginning of a scene.

Storyboards can answer questions like these:	What characters are in a frame of the movie, and how do they move? How does a scene begin? How does it end? What are the characters saying to each other? Are they saying anything? Where does a scene take place?

Answers

Pages 12 Narnia Riddles

1. Rings
2. Pools
3. Jadis
4. Strawberry
5. Aslan
6. Lamp-post
7. Narnia
8. Fledge
9. Apple
10. Orchard
11. Frank and Helen
12. Wardrobe

Page 14 The Magician's Nephew Wordsearch

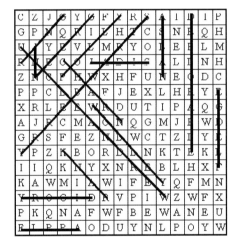

Page 18 The Lion, the Witch and the Wardrobe Crossword

1. Lampost
2. Tumnus
3. Beavers
4. Father Christmas
5. Stone Table
6. Turkish Delight
7. Professor Kirke
8. Wardrobe
9. Maugrim

Page 25 The Metal Tree

Page 27 The Horse and His Boy Wordsearch

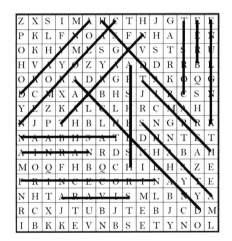

Answers

Page 30 Prince Caspian Crossword

Across	Down
3. DLF	1. Badger
4. Telmarine	2. Reepicheep
	5. Miraz

Page 32 Where Are We?
The children are in Narnia!
The ruins are Cair Paravel.

Page 34 In Search of the Gifts
Susan's horn isn't in the treasure chamber because she lost it when the children first returned to England and dropped it by the lamppost.

Page 36 Friends of Narnia Wordsearch

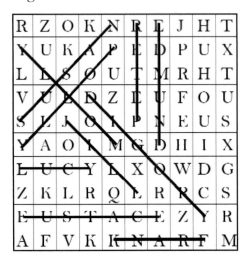

Page 39 Enemies of Aslan Crossword

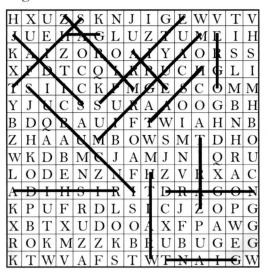

Pages 40 Through the Woods

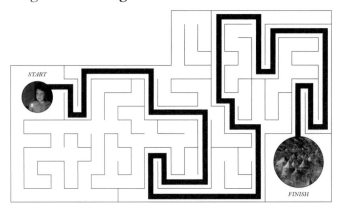

Page 44 Voyage of the Dawn Treader

Across	Down
4. Eustace	1. Dragon
5. Painting	2. Bern
	3. Ramandu

Answers

Page 45 True or False?

False. Eustace is spending the summer
with Edmund and Lucy.

True.

False. Reepicheep is looking for the end
of the world.

True.

True.

False. They believe the island is inhabited
by dragons.

True.

False. They find an island that turns
everything to gold.

False. She decides not to cast the spell.

True.

True.

True.

True.

False. It is full of lilies.

True.

Page 48 Narnia Riddles

JILL AND EUSTACE ARE LOOKING
FOR PRINCE RILIAN THE TRUE HEIR
TO THE THRONE

PUDDLEGLUM THE MARSHWIGGLE
HELPS THE CHILDREN LOOK FOR
PRINCE RILIAN

PUDDLEGLUM REFUSED TO GIVE
UP BELIEF IN ASLAN AND THE
OVERWORLD WHICH TURNED THE
QUEEN INTO A SERPENT THAT
THEY KILLED

Page 52 The Last Battle Wordsearch

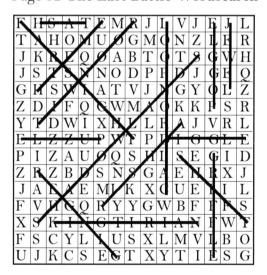

Page 47 The Silver Chair Wordsearch

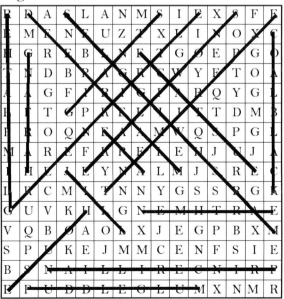

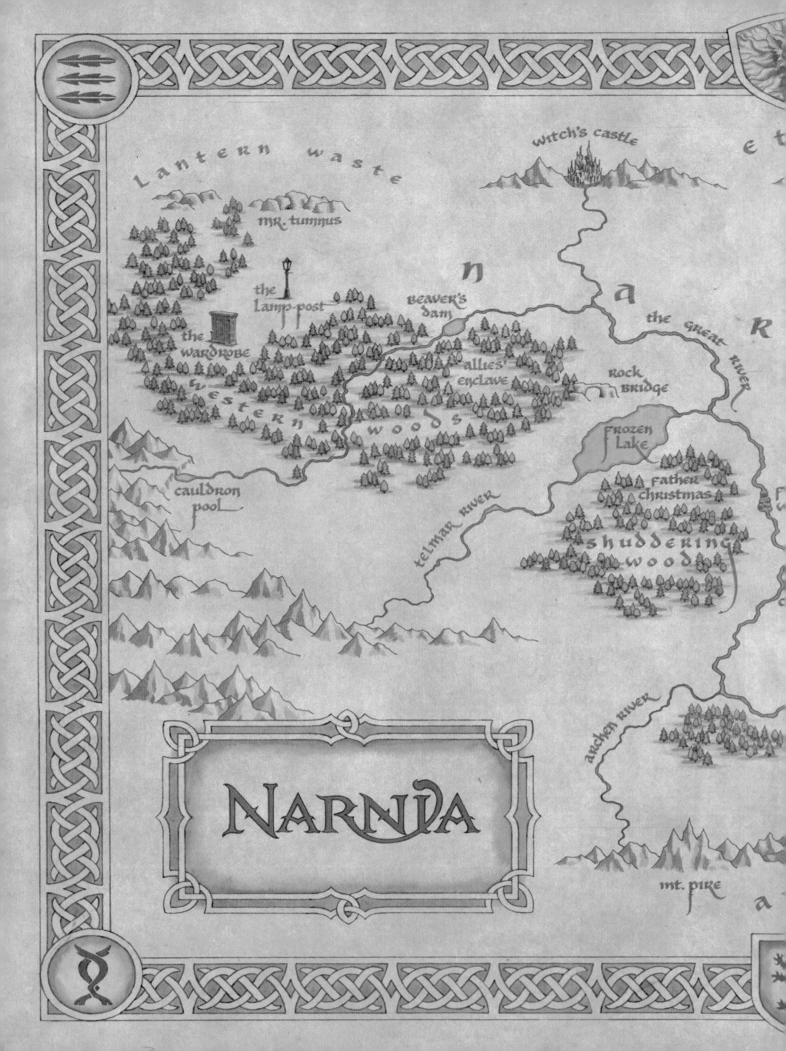

NARNIA